Ros Bayle

Action Raps

ACKNOWLEDGEMENTS

Written by: Ros Bayley
(in association with Lynn Broadbent)

Illustrated by: Peter Scott

Produced by: Lynda Lawrence.

Published by: Lawrence Educational
Unit 21 Brookvale Trading Estate,
Moor Lane, Birmingham,
West Midlands B6 7AQ

©   Lawrence Educational 2004.

ISBN: 1-903670-42-X

Introduction

We all need a sense of steady beat when performing any task involving sophisticated movement, i.e. when walking, dancing, writing, cutting with scissors, hammering in a nail or drawing. In fact, it is so essential that if someone lacks beat awareness, he or she usually have difficulty with both gross and fine motor skills.

Recent studies have even shown a correlation of beat competency to school achievement that exceeds that of either social class or mother's education, these latter two being the usual predictors of school success. By helping children to develop beat competency we can improve their chances of success.

There are a wide range of ways in which we can help children to develop beat competency, but the more that young children have opportunities to engage in singing, dancing and rapping and play with instruments, jingles and rhymes, the better they will get.

The rhymes in this book can all be chanted to a steady beat, or if you prefer, you can make up simple tunes to go with them. The important thing is simply to enjoy chanting them and to loose yourself in the musicality of language!

Ros Bayley

Introductory Rap

(This rap can be used to introduce any of the other raps)

If you're ready shout yes.

YES!

If you're steady shout yes.

YES!

If you're ready and you're steady shout yes, yes, yes.

YES, YES, YES!

Hands at the front.

Hands at the back.

Hands at the front,

Then clap, clap, clap.

Hands up high.

Hands down low,

Then wind the bobbin round

Let's go, go, go!

(Repeat)

Put your hands on your hips.

Sway from side to side.

Get on your pony

And ride, ride, ride.

Hold on tight

Down the street,

Stamp, stamp, stamp, stamp

Stamp your feet.

Point to the left, point to the right.

Thump the air with all your might.

Turn around, slap your thighs.

Run on the spot, lift your legs high.

Arms in the air, reach up high.

Higher and higher, touch the sky.

(Blow a whistle or make a whistle sound at the end of each section)

Wiggle your hips as you listen to the beat.
When the whistle blows sit back on your seat .... *whistle*!

Knock your knees as you listen to the beat.
When the whistle blows get back on your feet .... *whistle*!

Clap your hands as you listen to the beat.
When the whistle blows sit back on your seat .... *whistle*!

Stamp your feet as you listen to the beat.
When the whistle blows get back on your feet .... *whistle*!

Wobble like a jelly.

Swim like a fish.

Turn right around.

Blow a kiss.

Pull on a rope.

Arms in the air.

Clap your hands.

Comb your hair.

Move your arms,

Move your arms, up and down.

Swing your hips,

Swing your hips, round and round.

Move your fingers,

Move your fingers, wiggle them now.

Then stand up straight

And take a bow.

Spin like a helicopter

Going round and round.

Then bend right down

And touch the ground.

Now back up again

And run on the spot.

And keep on going

Till you hear me

shout......STOP!

(Each child will need a beanbag)

Put your beanbag on your knee.

Put your beanbag on your hair.

Put your beanbag on the floor,

And leave it there.

Turn right around.

Climb the stairs.

Pick your beanbag up

And throw it in the air!

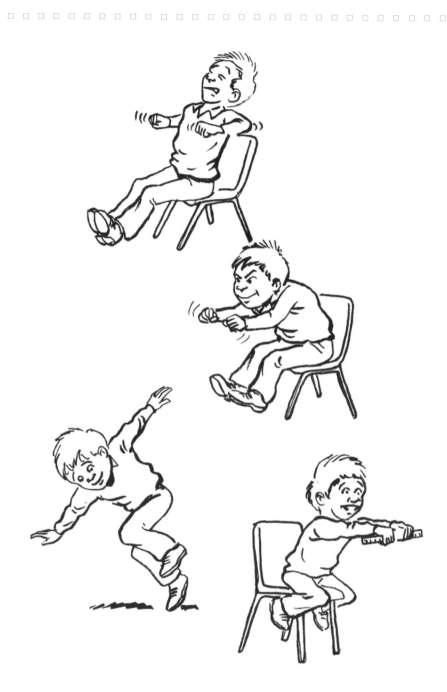

Row, row, row your boat,
Row as hard as you can.
Now hold on to the steering wheel
You're going to drive your van!

Fly, fly, fly your plane,
Fly as fast as you like.
Now hold onto the handlebars
As you ride your motorbike!

Row your boat.
Drive your van.
Fly the plane.
Ride your bike.
Just as fast as you like!

Bounce like a bouncing ball

Bouncing on the ground.

Turn like a roundabout

Going round and round.

Kick like a footballer

Trying to save a goal.

Slide like a fireman

Sliding down a pole.

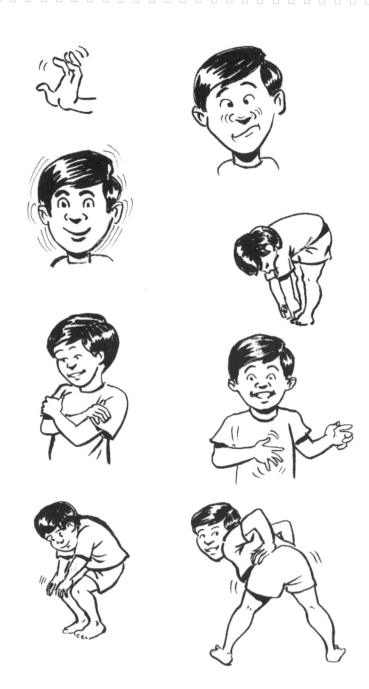

Wriggle your fingers.

Twitch your nose.

Shake your head.

Touch your toes.

Hold your arms.

Rub your tum.

Pat your knees.

Shake your bum.

Wiggle your fingers in the air.

Wiggle your fingers near the ground.

Put your hands on your hips and move them round and round.

Lunge to the left.

Lunge to the right.

Hold onto the string and Fly your kite.

(The children work in pairs, holding hands and facing each other)

Swing your arms,

Swing your arms,

Swing your arms, to-ge-ther.

Pat your hands,

Pat your hands,

Pat your hands, to-ge-ther.

Stamp your feet,

Stamp your feet,

Stamp your feet, to-ge-ther.

Now walk around in a circle

Creeping as light as a feather.

Put one hand on your head.
Put one hand on your nose.
Now swap them over
And touch your toes.

Put one hand at the front.
Put one hand at the back.
Now swap them over
Then clap, clap, clap.

Put one hand on your nose.
Put one hand on your ear.
Now swap them over
Then wipe a tear.

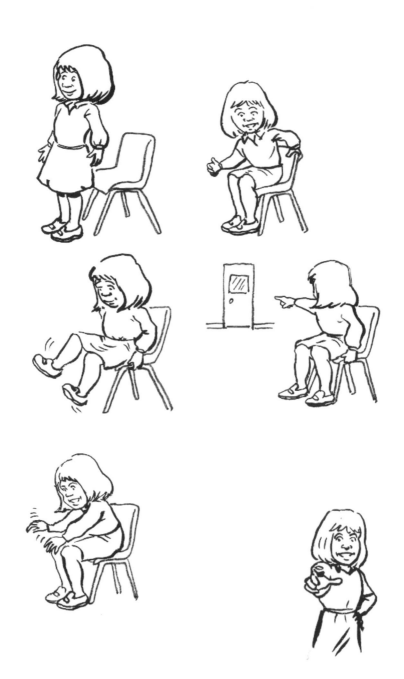

(You will need a chair for each child)

Stand up, sit down, stand up,
Sit down, stand up, sit down,
and stamp on the floor.

Stand up, sit down, stand up,
Sit down, stand up, sit down,
and point at the door.

Stand up, sit down, stand up,
Sit down, now pat your
knees, now pat your knees.

Stand up, sit down, stand up,
Sit down, stand up, sit down,
then point at me!

We hope you have enjoyed this rap book.

Other books in the same series are:

Ros Bayley's **Animal Raps**   ISBN: 1-903670-38-1

Ros Bayley's **Action Raps**   ISBN: 1-903670-42-X

Ros Bayley's **Beanbag Raps**   ISBN: 1-903670-43-8

Ros Bayley's **Noisy Raps**   ISBN: 1-903670-44-6

Additional rhymes and further guidance on developing children's beat competency can be found in our '**Helping Young Children With Steady Beat**' resource pack.

Included with this pack is a small cuddly toy called BEAT BABY, who can be used at the beginning and end of sessions to help focus the children and to bring emotional engagement to the whole process.

ISBN: 1-903670-26-8

For further details of these and our many other publications, visit our website:

www.educationalpublications.com